# MOSES SUPPOSES

The Bible
as told to
Dan Greenburg

# MOSES SUPPOSES

The Bible
as told to
Dan Greenburg

## DAN GREENBURG

BARRICADE BOOKS, INC.
New York, N.Y.

Published by Barricade Books Inc.
150 Fifth Avenue, New York, NY 10011

Printed in the United States of America.

Library of Congress Cataloging-in-Publication Data
Greenburg, Dan.
    Moses supposess : the Bible as told to Dan Greenburg / Dan Greenburg
          p.    cm.
  ISPN 1-56980-100-2
  1. Bible.  O.T.—History of Biblical events—Fiction.  2. Bible.  O.T.—
History of Biblical events—Humor.  3. Moses (Biblical leader)—Fiction.
4. Moses (Biblical leader)—Humor.  I. Title.
PS3557.R379M6  1997
813'.54—dc21                          96-51914
                                     CIP

10 9 8 7 6 5 4 3 2 1

# TABLE OF CONTENTS

# CREATION

**IN THE BEGINNING**, God took a week off and created the world.

On the first day, He created the heaven and the earth. Darkness was upon the face of the deep; and God said, "Let there be light!" and there was light. And God saw the light and knew that it was good, especially for reading in bed after dinner, and He divided the light from the darkness.

"The light shall I call Day," He said, "and the darkness shall I call . . . um, either Nocturnal Void or some other name which shall occur to me before bedtime." And that was the first day.

On the second day, God got up early and had a hearty breakfast. Then He made the firmament and divided the waters which were under the firmament from the waters which were above the firmament. "The firmament shall I call Heaven," said God, "and the waters shall I call Waters."

On the third day, God had a bagel and tea and then got right down to work. "O.K. now, where was I?" He said. "Oh, right. Let the waters under the heaven be gathered unto one place, and let the dry land appear. And the dry land shall I call Earth." Then He let the earth bring forth grass, and herb-yielding seed, and tree-yielding fruit, and that was pretty much all he felt like doing on the third day, having made early dinner plans.

On the fourth day, God made the seasons, the sun, the moon, the stars, the planets, the asteroids, the comets, the constellations, the black holes, the galaxies, and the unimaginably infinite reaches of the cosmos. Kind of a busy day. God was bushed.

On the fifth day, God made the fish and the fowl, which was considerably easier than what he'd done the day before, and it allowed him to knock off early.

On the sixth day, God said, "Let the earth bring forth living creatures, including Man. And let Man have dominion over the fish of the sea and over the fowl of the air and over the cattle and over every creeping thing that creepeth over the earth. And

I shall make Man in my image and likeness, except maybe without the beard and with smaller ears."

He didn't know what to name the first man. At first He thought He'd name him Bruce. Then He thought Sheldon or Rudy or maybe Skippy. Finally He decided on Adam. For Adam He created a wondrous place called the Garden of Eden, and in it a garden apartment condo for Adam to live in, complete with wraparound patio, wood-burning fireplace, and a fully stocked minibar.

God had never made a man before. He knew that Adam was not perfect, but he had certainly turned out better than either mosquitoes or dry rot.

# THE GARDEN OF EDEN

"**SO, ADAM,**" said God, "how dost thou like it here?"

"Oh, it's cool here, sire," said Adam. "It's the best place I've ever been."

"It's the *only* place thou hast ever been," said God.

"Well, that too," said Adam.

"Anything thou needest," said God, "pick up the phone and giveth a holler. It's a local call."

"Well, sire," said Adam shyly, "now that you mention it, there *was* one thing . . . "

"Yes?" said God.

"Where does a guy go around here to meet babes?"

God chuckled.

"Eden hath no singles bars," He said, "so there are no places to, as you put it, 'meet babes.' Dost thou know why there are no places to meet babes, Adam?"

"Tell me," said Adam.

"Because I have not thusfar created any babes."

"Makes sense," said Adam.

"Wouldst thou like me to create a babe for thee?" said God.

"You mean You could actually do that, sire?" said Adam, impressed.

God nodded, smiling.

"I am the Supreme Being," He said. "I can do anything I wish, even blow smoke rings. Wouldst thou like me to create a mate for thee?"

Adam thought this over.

"Yeah, sure," said Adam. "I mean, either that or ESPN."

"Very well then," said God, "I shall now create thee a mate. Behold!"

He took a rib from Adam's side and went right to work.

"Ow!" said Adam, "that hurt! What did you do that for?"

But God did not reply. He was busy adding stuff to Adam's rib, making it a woman, humming to Himself as He worked.

Pretty soon He was done. In front of Adam stood a beautiful young woman.

"Adam, this is, uh . . . Edie," said God. "No, no, not Edie. Eve. Eve, this is Adam."

"Hey, Eve," said Adam, "how's it going?"

"Not too shabby," said Eve.

"Let not the fact that you are both naked cause you to be ashamed," said God.

Adam checked Eve out.

"Nothing to be ashamed of *there*," said Adam.

"Or there, either," said Eve, checking Adam out.

"So, Eve," said Adam, "what do you say? You want to maybe come back to my place for awhile?"

"What for?" said Eve.

"Oh, I don't know," said Adam. "Have a white wine spritzer for starters. Then maybe, you know, cleave together and begin propagating humankind?"

"Yeah, why not?" said Eve. "I mean what else have I got to do, right?"

"Be fruitful and multiply, my children," said God. "Enjoy the facilities. Everything has been comped. In return I ask but one thing."

"You name it, sire, you got it," said Adam.

"Whatever ye do," said God, "partaketh not of the fruit on that tree over there, or ye shall surely die."

"What's the matter," said Eve, "pesticides?"

"No, no," said God. "That tree is the tree of knowledge of good and evil. Eat of its fruit and I shall be wrathful and cranky beyond measure."

"Hey, no problem," said Adam.

God was well pleased with His creations.

On the seventh day God was too pooped to do anymore. So He kicked back, took the day off, pronounced it Sabbath, sanctified it, and ordered takeout Chinese food.

# THE EXPULSION FROM EDEN

**IN THE GARDEN OF EDEN** at first everything was copacetic. And aside from getting scalded in the shower when the other guy flushed the toilet, Adam and Eve were well pleased with one another.

Then one day Eve was strolling past the tree of knowledge and heard a sly voice.

"Hey, baby, what's up?"

It was a serpent, who was coiled around the tree.

"Say, you're a foxy lady," said the serpent.

"If that's a compliment, thanks," said Eve.

"You know," said the serpent, "you're the foxiest lady I've ever seen."

"How many ladies have you seen?" said Eve.

"Yeah. So how's old Adam treating you?" said the serpent.

"You don't hear me complaining."

"And how do you like it here?"

"It ain't Club Med, but it's nice," said Eve.

"So tell me," said the serpent. "You eat from any good trees lately?"

"Every one but the tree of knowledge of good and evil," said Eve.

"And why not that one, babe?"

"God said if we ate from that one we would surely die."

The serpent laughed.

"That God," he said. "What a character! You won't *die* if you eat from that tree, sugar. All that'll happen is your eyes will be opened, your innocence will fade, and you will know both good and evil. It's a rush!"

"Really?" said Eve.

"Trust me," said the serpent. "Take a bite and see."

Eve was dubious.

"I don't know," she said.

"Just try a nibble," said the serpent. "You don't like it, spit it out."

Eve was tempted.

"I guess a nibble couldn't hurt," she said.

Eve nibbled an apple from the tree of knowledge.

"Mmmmm," she said.

"Well?" said the serpent.

"It tastes like . . . chicken," she said.

"But you didn't die, right?" said the serpent.

"No, but I . . . Yikes!" she cried out. "I'm naked here!"

"So?"

"So?" said Eve. "So you can see my boobs and my tush!"

The serpent nodded and smiled.

Eve took off for the apartment. When she arrived, Adam was reading the sports pages.

"Adam," she said, arriving out of breath, "taste this and tell me what you think."

"If it's spoiled, take it back," said Adam without looking up.

"It's not spoiled," said Eve. "I just wanted you to taste it."

Adam tasted it. Then he frowned and raised his eyebrows.

"Holy Toledo!" he said. "We're walking around naked as jay-birds here! Do you realize that?"

"Before eating that apple I was unashamed of my naked-ness," said Eve. "Now, having eaten it, I have an uncontrollable urge to . . . shop!"

"What was in that apple anyway?" Adam demanded.

Eve began to cry.

"The serpent said it would be O.K.," said Eve.

Adam slapped his forehead.

"The *serpent* said?" he shouted. "Eve, don't tell me you ate the fruit of the tree of knowledge!"

"We both ate it," said Eve.

"Hoo boy," said Adam. "We have really put our foot in it now, kiddo!"

The following morning Adam and Eve were walking in the garden. They had fashioned garments out of fig leaves and nylon polyester spandex to clothe their nakedness.

Suddenly they heard a voice:

"Good day, my children," it said.

"Jiggers, it's God!" said Adam.

"Adam? Eve? Where are ye?" called God.

"Over here," said Adam.

"Oh, *there* ye are," said God. Then He frowned. "Pray, why

hast ye covered thyselves in fig leaves and nylon polyester spandex?"

Adam and Eve looked at each other.

"Well?" said God. "I'm waiting."

"We, uh, were just trying to clothe our nakedness, sire," said Eve.

"Who told ye that ye were naked?" thundered God.

"N-nobody, sire," said Eve. "I just happened to be passing a mirror, and I caught sight of my boobs, and I thought, 'Hey, how about that, I'm naked,' you know?"

"Hast thou eaten of the tree, whereof I specifically commanded thee that thou shouldst not eat, under penalty of death or divine crankiness?"

"It wasn't my fault, sire!" cried Adam. "Eve tricked me!"

"It wasn't my fault either, sire!" cried Eve. "The snake tricked *me!*"

"I did not!" hissed the serpent.

"Did, too!" yelled Eve.

"Did not!"

"Did, too!"

"Stop!" shouted God. "I'm disgusted with all three of ye!"

"So are we grounded or what?" said Adam.

"Grounded?" shouted God. "Grounded? *I'll* give ye grounded. O.K., here's how it's going to be. Serpent, because thou hast instigated this, thou art cursed above all cattle and above every beast of the field. Upon thy belly shalt thou go henceforth!"

"Oh right," muttered the serpent. "Like *that'll* be a big change."

"Woman," said God, "in sorrow shalt thou bring forth children, and when they are old enough to speak, I only hope they treat thee the way that thou hast treated me!"

"Sire," said Eve, "may I say I'm sorry?"

"'Sorry' doesn't cut it anymore, cookie!" thundered the Diety to Eve. And to Adam he said, "Because thou hast eaten of the tree of knowledge, despite clearly posted warnings, cursed will be the ground on which thou treadest. And when thou toilest in the fields, the bulk of what thou earnest by the sweat of thy brow shall be confiscated from thee in the form of tithes and levies, and most of thy legitimate business deductions shall be disallowed!"

Then God produced a flaming sword and pointed it at the gates of Eden.

"And now," said God, "get out of my sight, the lot of ye!"

"But, sire," said Adam, "where shall we go?"

"Oh, go to Babylon or Newark for all I care," said God.

Adam turned to Eve.

"Well, I hope *you're* happy," he said.

"Oh, cut me some slack," said Eve.

# CAIN AND ABEL

**AND IT CAME TO PASS** that Adam and Eve had knowledge of each other and bore two sons, Cain and Abel.

The firstborn, Cain, was a tiller of the ground, and the secondborn, Abel, was a keeper of sheep. And Cain brought of the fruit of the ground an offering to the Lord. And the Lord said, "O.K., thanks, Cain, just leave it on the credenza there. I'm busy paying bills."

And Abel brought to the Lord the firstlings of his flock and of the fat thereof. And the Lord said, "Now that's nifty, firstlings of thy flock and of the fat thereof; way to go, my man!" and gave Abel a high-five.

And Cain was wroth that the Lord had shewed respect to Abel's offering but not to his, and his countenance fell unto the ground.

And the Lord said unto Cain, "Why so glum, chum?"

And Cain replied, "Oh, leave me alone."

And Cain was grouchy beyond all measure and did talk with Abel his brother in the field, saying, "Mom, Dad, and God like you better than me."

Then Cain did rise up against Abel and slew him.

And the Lord said unto Cain, "Where is Abel, thy brother?"

And Abel replied, "I know not; what am I, my brother's keeper or something?"

And God replied, "Cain, what hast thou done? The voice of thy brother's blood crieth unto me from the ground."

"So if you already knew," said Cain, "why ask?"

"Behold," thundered the Lord, "killing your brother was bad enough, but wising off to the Supreme Diety pretty much tears it. Therefore shall my mark be upon thee. Thou art now cursed from the earth, which hath opened her mouth to receive thy brother's blood from thy hand. A fugitive shalt thou be on the earth, yet none shall create a TV series about thee. And if whilst flying, a dove should experience the need to relieve itself, its waste will surely be directed to thine head. And if thou enterest a lottery, thou wouldst be a ten-million-dollar winner but lose thy ticket down a subway grate before collecting. Also shalt thou be stricken with gastritis, hypoglycemia, and—shouldst thou ever acquire a computer or play tennis—carpal tunnel syndrome."

Thus chastened, Cain did flee to dwell in the land of Nod, located East of Eden, which was the title of a book by John Steinbeck and a movie starring James Dean.

And we are told that Cain took a wife, who bore him a son named Enoch, but we are not told where he could have found her, since at that point there were only two other people left in the world besides Cain, unless she was either his mother or a new sister maybe.

# NOAH AND THE ARK

**MANY YEARS HAD PASSED.** The world was populated by hordes of people with dubious morals. Since they were probably all the progeny of Cain and a close family member, this is not surprising.

And the Lord said, "Yea, verily, I am highly displeased with mankind. I shall therefore remove him from the face of the earth. Only Noah shall I spare, who, although admittedly something of a lush, is a just man, a good husband, a loving father, and not a bad little dancer."

And God said unto Noah, who was then 600 years of age, "The end of mankind is imminent; for I shall soon cause it to rain for forty days and forty nights and subsequently bring upon the earth a flood of waters to destroy all flesh, both of man and of beast, and additionally all beachfront property that is in the Hamptons.

"Only thee shall I spare, and those whom thou lovest and wouldst bring with thee, and they shall escape this flood by means of an ark that I shall cause thee to fashion, the length of which shall be 300 cubits, the breadth of which shall be 50 cubits, the height of which shall be 30 cubits, and having as its means of propulsion this really humongous outboard motor. Pray, what would be thy suggestions of whom to take upon such a vessel to repropagate the earth when flood waters recede?"

"Well," said Noah, "I know a group of exotic dancers from the Kit Kat Klub who would be really nifty breeders."

"What I was thinking," said the Lord, "was two of each and every species of living thing upon the earth, the male and his female, including fowls, beasts, cattle, and every thing that doth creep upon the earth, like cockroaches, maggots, centipedes, dung beetles, and including even divorce court judges."

And so it was that Noah began building the ark, abetted by a detailed set of plans and an Ark Kit provided by the Lord, and with the assistance of his three sons, Ham, Shem, and Curly. And passersby did snigger and point, chiding Noah for his belief that a major flood was about to transpire, although no more than sprinkles had been forecast by Willard Scott.

And when the ark was completed, and when Noah began leading pairs of lions, lizards, ladybugs, wallabies, wildebeest, manatees, mantises, scorpions, hyenas, budgies, and teacup Yorkshire terriers up the gangplank into the ark, he was cited for violating animal husbandry ordinances and overwhelmed by sales reps from Hartz Mountain Wild Animal Chow.

And when all of the animals and all of the members of Noah's and Ham's and Shem's and Curly's family had been loaded into the ark, it finally commenced to rain.

And the rains came down, and the rivers overflowed their banks, and on certain corners did vendors begin a brisk business in funny little umbrella hats that you wear right on your head. And townspeople who had previously mocked and chided Noah now banged on the ark's door, attempting to nullify previous sniggers, fruitlessly trying to suck up to Noah, but it availed them not.

Forty days and forty nights did it rain, and forty days and forty nights did Noah and his family fruitlessly attempt to change litter boxes, and they mourned the fact that God had provided but one window in the vessel of their deliverance and no air fresheners.

And the waters prevailed upon the earth 150 days, and then the windows of heaven were closed and the rains did cease, and the waters decreased, and in the tenth month of their journey did the tops of mountains become once more visible.

And Noah released a raven from the window of the ark to try and locate dry land, but in the evening when it returned, quoth the raven "Nevermore." And seven days thereafter Noah sent forth a budgie, and that bird did return to him in the evening with an olive in her beak, which Noah took as a sign that Happy Hour had begun and plopped it into his first martini following the Deluge.

And the waters which had covered the earth receded and the ark came to rest atop Mount Ararat. And Noah opened the door of the ark, and all living things which had resided in the ark went forth from it. And the Lord said, "Never again shall I lift my hand to curse or smite either man nor beast, for I am no longer cranky. So go be fruitful and multiply, live long and prosper."

# ABRAHAM AND SARAH BEAR A SON

**AND IT CAME TO PASS** that the progeny of Noah and of Ham and Shem and Curly begat more progeny, and their progeny begat again more progeny, and before long their progeny had once more repopulated the earth and then some.

And one of the descendants of Noah, whose name was Abraham, did impress the Almighty with his goodness. And God said unto Abraham, "I shall bless thee and make thy name great and make of thee and thy seed a great nation. Also shall I hire a P.R. man to spread word of your greatness and possibly even book you on Letterman, although that depends so much upon the whim of talent coordinators."

And Abraham said unto the Lord, "You mentioned seed. But the fact is that my wife Sarah and I are both seedless and childless, although we have consulted fertility experts of all stripes and attempted in vitro fertilization, finally accepting that we were too old and therefore barren. We sublimated our thwarted parental longings with a pussycat."

And God said unto Abraham, "How can I make of thee a great nation and found it upon a pussycat?"

And Abraham replied, "You have a point there."

And God said, "O.K., tell you what. I shall cause thy wife Sarah to be with child, regardless of her age. How old *are* you guys, by the way?"

And Abraham said, "Well, Sarah is ninety, and I'm a hundred."

And God said, "Oy vey."

And Abraham said, "So does this mean the deal is off or what?"

And God said, "No, no, I was just thinking whether a great nation might indeed be founded upon a pussycat. But a deal is a deal. So shall thy wife Sarah indeed conceive and bear a child."

Sarah overheard this conversation and giggled.

And so it came to pass that a baby was indeed born to Sarah

and Abraham. And they called his name Isaac. And it was bottle-fed, in case you were wondering. And Abraham, obeying his covenant with the Lord, caused Isaac and himself and all the male members of his household to be circumcised, which made everybody kind of testy for about a week or so.

# SODOM AND GOMORRAH

**NOW ABRAHAM'S NEPHEW LOT** dwelled in the city of Sodom, the sister city of Gomorrah. And the inhabitants of Sodom and Gomorrah were of dubious moral fiber and total shmendricks, which sorely vexed the Almighty.

And God appeared to Abraham and said unto him, "The inhabitants of the twin cities Sodom and Gomorrah do vex Me sorely. Feh! I'm thinking seriously about nuking the entire population."

"I thought you were through nuking entire populations," said Abraham.

"No, no," said God, "that just covered floods; this time it'll be fire and brimstone. It's different."

"Ethnic cleansing by whatever means contains the same scour power," said Abraham.

"Yeah, well, so I changed My mind," said God.

"You don't mind my saying so," said Abraham, "I think you got a couple anger issues you ought to look at."

"Yeah," said God, "but these people are vexing Me sorely, and people who vex God sorely always run the risk of annihilation. I mean that's one of the perks of being God."

"Then wilt Thou also destroy the righteous along with the wicked?" asked Abraham.

"What dost thou mean?" said God.

"I mean say there are fifty righteous men in the twin-city metroplex of Sodom and Gomorrah. Wouldst Thou destroy fifty righteous men along with the shmendricks?"

"Fifty?" said God. "O.K. If thou canst find me fifty righteous men in Sodom, I'll spare the city."

"Really?" said Abraham. "How's about forty-five?"

"O.K.," said God. "Forty-five and Sodom is spared."

"How's forty?" said Abraham.

"This bargaining is beginning to irritate me," said the Almighty, "but for forty righteous men I shall spare the city, too. Forty, and not one man less than forty."

"Thirty," said Abraham. "Tell me you'll wipe out thirty just men—thirty real sweethearts, thirty pussycats—just because the rest are shmendricks. Tell me that."

"I'm beginning to get sorely vexed at *thee* here," said the Almighty. "But, all right, for thirty I'll cancel the conflagration, but that's it."

"I don't mean to low-ball you," said Abraham, "but I'm thinking of a number and I want you to tell me if it's even a remote possibility. You don't need to answer right away, you can sleep on it."

"Boy, thou art really tickling the tiger's tail here, Abe," said God. "Let me save thee a lot of trouble and tell thee my best offer right now, O.K.? Ten. Ten is my absolute rock-bottom lowest figure. Find me ten righteous men, and I spare Sodom. Any less than ten, or anymore bargaining, and I nuke everybody now, including thou. Kapeesh?"

"Kapeesh," said Abraham.

And so God dispatched two angels to the city of Sodom to find ten righteous men. But, aside from Lot and his family, the angels found naught but shmendricks, and so God marked the city for destruction.

And God said unto Abraham, "Taketh thy family and the family of thy brother's son Lot, and let them flee Sodom, for lo, this city is history!  And warn them not to look back at the city's destruction, for whosoever doth look back shall surely be turned into a pillar of salt!"

And so Abraham and his family and Lot and his family fled Sodom. And the Lord God rained down fire and brimstone and destruction and napalm and Agent Orange upon the cities of Sodom and Gomorrah. But Lot's wife looked back upon the conflagration, and she was instantly turned into a pillar of salt.

"Dang!" said Lot, who was mightily disappointed to see his wife thus transformed. Although tempted to take her with him anyhow, Lot finally decided against it, having recently been put on a very low-sodium diet.

# ABRAHAM SACRIFICES ISAAC

**ONE DAY GOD** decided to put Abraham to a little test.

"Abraham," said God, "I have a job for thee. Take thy son Isaac whom thou lovest and go to the land of Moriah and offer him up as a burnt offering on one of the mountains there."

"You're *kidding* me," said Abraham.

"Nope," said God, "this is a real deal."

Abraham was sorely vexed by this request, but too polite to argue with God. So he rose up in the morning, saddled his ass, threw firewood and little Isaac across the saddle, and hightailed it up to Moriah.

And Isaac said to his father, "Hey, Pop, I see the wood for the burnt offering, but I don't see the lamb for the sacrifice. What's going down?"

And Abraham said, "My son, God said He'd provide a lamb for the sacrifice is all I know."

When they reached Moriah, Abraham built the altar and placed the wood upon it. Then he took little Isaac, bound his hands and feet together, and placed him atop the wood.

"Uh, Pop?" said little Isaac. "Is there something you'd like to tell me?"

"No, not really," said Abraham with a heavy heart.

Abraham took out a ginsu knife and held it to little Isaac's throat. Just then an ear-splitting tone was heard, and a voice said:

"This is a test. If it had been an actual request to sacrifice thy son, thou wouldst have been directed to another frequency and given emergency instructions."

The voice did not sound like the voice of God.

"And with whom would I have the pleasure of speaking?" asked Abraham.

"Oh, hi," said the voice. "I'm Maury, an angel of the Almighty? God is sorry He couldn't be here in person, but He was abruptly called off to an early business lunch. He sends his regrets and the following message: 'Dear Abraham: Lay not thine hand upon the lad nor do thou any thing to him of a permanent nature, for now I know that thou respecteth Me, seeing as how thou hast not withheld even thine only son, whose name be . . . fill in name of son.' Oh, sorry. And God continues: 'Because thou hast done this thing, I shall bless thee, multiply thy seed as the stars of the heaven and the grains of sand upon the seashore, etcetera etcetera. Yours faithfully, God. P.S. There's a ram in the thicket for your sacrifice, and a peanut-butter-and-jelly sandwich for the kid. Enjoy.'"

# ESAU SELLS HIS BIRTHRIGHT

**AND IT CAME TO PASS** that Isaac grew up and married a woman named Rebecca, and she bore him twin sons. The firstborn twin was big and strong and as hairy as a chimp, and they did name him Esau. The second, who was born six minutes later, was smooth as a bikini wax, and him they did name Jacob.

Esau grew to be a cunning hunter and a shtarker who could do a hundred marine pushups and press his own weight with a Gold's Gym barbell. Jacob grew up to be a nerd and a couch potato who developed a paunch and early male-pattern baldness and became the founding president of Hair Club for Men.

Isaac had an extensive collection of the Village People's albums and liked macho men, so he preferred Esau. Rebecca liked sissies and preferred Jacob.

One day before dawn, Esau went into the weight room and did three hours of bench presses, military curls, and special drills to define his lats and traps and triceps. When he finished, he was dripping sweat and starved for a hearty breakfast.

"Hey, Jake," said Esau to his twin brother, "I'm so hungry here, man, my stomach thinks my throat's cut. Whattaya got for breakfast?"

"Well," said Jacob, "I am personally about to enjoy a tempting bowl of Bite-Size Frosted Mini-Wheats."

"Hey, that should really hit the spot," said Esau. "Rustle up one for me, too."

"Sorry, guy," said Jacob, "there's only the one bowl left here, and it's got my name on it. Why don't you run out to the corner and order an Egg McMuffin?"

"Get serious," said Esau. "I'm fainting from hunger here. I'm the firstborn, and I claim that bowl of Bite-Size Frosted Mini-Wheats as my birthright."

"Your birthright means zip at the breakfast table, Bunkie," said Jacob. "Unless of course you'd like to trade it for grub."

"What are you saying," said Esau, "that you'd give me your bowl of Bite-Size Frosted Mini-Wheats in exchange for my birthright?"

"Yep."

Now Esau may have been a cunning hunter who was able to press his own weight, but he also had the IQ of a radish.

"O.K., deal," said Esau. "Taps, no take-backs."

And so it was that Esau traded his birthright for a breakfast loaded with empty calories.

# JACOB TAKES ESAU'S BLESSING

**ISAAC GREW AGED,** and his eyesight failed him. One day as he lay dying, he called for Esau and said, "My son, I feel that my hours on this mortal coil are numbered. Before I die, I should like to give you my blessing, my sheep, my goats, my camels, my slaves, and my mutual funds. But first I should like you to go out and kill a deer and cook me up one of your famous venison pot pies."

"You got it, Pop," said Esau. He took his bow and arrow and went out in search of deer.

But Rebecca had been listening, and she wanted her beloved Jacob to receive her husband's blessing and diversified stock portfolio instead of Esau.

"Jacob," she said, "thy father is about to expire and cede his estate to thine Neanderthal elder sibling. What do you say we sneak you in there first, disguised as Esau, and beat him out?"

"How could we accomplish that?" said Jacob. "My brother and I are not even remotely similar. E.g., my brother Esau is a hairy man, and I am a smooth man. We don't even smell the same."

Rebecca, though a world-class matriarch and a member of the Biblical Moms Hall of Fame, had a code of ethics which was indistinguishable from that of Imelda Marcos.

"Behold," said Rebecca, extracting a set of Esau's ripe and sopping sweats from a Hefty trash bag. "Put these on. They are saturated with enough Eau d'Esau to fell a skunk at fifty paces."

"But my brother Esau is a hairy man," protested Jacob, "and I—despite my completely natural and undetectable rug from Hair Club for Men—am a smooth man."

"Behold," she said, extracting a custom-made set of forearm merkins from a drawer. "Put these on, and you could play Roddy McDowall in *Planet of the Apes*."

And so she dressed Jacob in Esau's ripe sweats and the custom-made arm toupees. Then she went out to the freezer in the garage, took out a frozen venison Hungry Man TV dinner, and popped it in the microwave. Then she sent Jacob in to receive his dying father's blessing.

"Whooh!" said Isaac as Jacob entered the room. "That's either my favorite son Esau, returned early from the hunt, or else Rebecca's let the camels into the living room again."

"Hi, Pop," said Jacob, handing his dad the venison pot pie, "here's lunch."

"The smell is the smell of Esau," said Isaac, "but the voice is the voice of Jacob. Come near so that I might feel thee."

And Jacob went near to his father, and Isaac felt up his son's forearms.

"Well, you may *sound* like your fruity younger brother," said Isaac, "but you *feel* like Esau, and you smell like him as well, God help you, and two out of three ain't bad."

"That's what I'm saying," said Jacob.

"Right," said Isaac. "O.K., you're Esau, and I'm a monkey's father. And so, being of sound mind and body, I hereby bequeath to you everything that is mine—livestock, real estate, and, most importantly, the title of Third and Final Founding Patriarch of the Judeo-Christian Religion Group. Also, oh yes, blessed be all those that bless thee, and cursed be all that curse thee, and here are my season passes to the Meadowlands. And now, for God's sake, go take a shower!"

And so Jacob, having tricked his father into receiving his blessing, withdrew to cackle and gloat.

A short while later, the real Esau appeared to his father, bearing a steaming venison pot pie.

"How's it goin', Pop?" said Esau. "Here's lunch."

"I thought I sent you off to the showers," said Isaac.

"Excuse me?" said Esau.

"You already gave me lunch, I gave you my blessing, and now, although, I hate to eat and run, I've got to get some serious dying done here, so run along."

After much touching and feeling and sniffing, Esau proved his identity to his father, who promptly had a myocardial infarction and expired. When Esau, who had the intelligence of spinach, was finally able to grasp how badly he'd been hornswoggled, he vowed to disembowel his younger sibling forthwith.

Rebecca gave Jacob a fake I.D. and got him into the government's witness protection program for as long as it might take for Esau's ire to cool sufficiently for Jacob to return to his homeland.

# JACOB AND RACHEL AND LEAH

**THE WITNESS PROTECTION PROGRAM** sent Jacob to the land of Padan-aram, where he ultimately found lodging with his Uncle Laban.

Now Laban was possessed of a beauteous younger daughter whose name was Rachel, and a less beauteous older daughter whose name was Leah. And Jacob was instantly smitten with Rachel, even though she was his cousin. Jacob asked his Uncle Laban for Rachel's hand in marriage.

"Tell you what," said Laban. "I'd sort of had my heart set on marrying her off to someone outside of the family, but if you're willing to earn her, I'll not withhold my blessing."

"And, pray, Uncle Laban," said Jacob, "how might I earn your daughter's hand in marriage?"

"By toiling for me in the fields for seven years," said Laban.

Now Jacob was a nerd and a couch potato, but Rachel had a body that wouldn't quit.

"It's a done deal," said Jacob, and Laban produced a contract, which he'd had the foresight to draw up, and Jacob did sign it without looking at the fine print.

And so it came to pass that Jacob toiled for Laban for a full seven years. And when the seven years work contract had been fulfilled, Laban threw a huge wedding, complete with pigs-in-blankets hors d'oeuvres and a man playing "Hava Nagila" and "Lady of Spain" on the accordion.

The bride was led up to the chuppah, hidden by the traditional white veil. When it came time to kiss the bride, Jacob raised the veil and got the shock of his life—he had married not his beloved Rachel but her older sister Leah, who, although a lovely person with many fine qualities, was frankly something of a bow-wow.

"Hey, what the heck is going on here?" said Jacob. "I worked seven years to marry Rachel, not Leah. I mean I signed a contract and everything."

"You didn't check the fine print," said Laban. "In the boiler-plate it says that in this country to give a younger daughter in marriage while the firstborn remains unwed constitutes a class-A felony."

"But you have deceived me by substituting Leah for Rachel," cried Jacob.

"Oh, right," said Laban. "Like we don't know why the witness protection program sent you here in the first place. Well, the chickens have come home to roost."

Jacob knew he'd been snookered fair and square.

"Tell you what," said Laban. "You sign the option clause in the wedding contract here to work seven more years, and you can have Rachel in just one week, no money down, zero interest and no payments till the first of the year, plus I'll throw in for absolutely no extra work time Leah's handmaidens Bilhah and Zilpah who once modeled industrial lingerie for International Harvester."

Jacob knew he was getting the shaft, but he could make out Rachel's bod through her bridesmaid's dress, and he didn't hate the idea of having four wives, and so he signed, and everybody ate more pigs-in-blankets and drank lots of cheap Manischewitz Chardonnay.

# JOSEPH AND
# THE COAT OF MANY COLORS

**NOW JACOB MOVED** to the land of Canaan with his wives Rachel and Leah and Bilhah and Zilpah and all of their children, of which there were already eleven; and their names were Reuben, Simeon, Levi, Judah, Issachar, Zebulun, Dan, Naphtali, Gad, and Asher, and don't even ask how they fit everything into the station wagon.

And after Joseph, a final son was born, and his name was Benjamin, but Joseph was his father's favorite, and the old man did spoil him rotten, and Jacob bought the boy a coat of many colors by Benetton.

"My brothers," cried Joseph, "come and admire the token of parental esteem our father has bestowed upon me."

"That coat makes you look like a dork," said Issachar.

"Not even Pee Wee Herman or Richard Simmons would wear a coat like that," said Naphtali.

"Well then," said Joseph, "let me tell you a dream I had. I dreamed we were all in the fields, tying up bundles of wheat, and my bundle was standing upright, but all of *your* bundles came and bowed down to mine."

"So what are you saying?" said Asher. "You think that we should all bow down to you or what?"

"Oh, but that was merely my dream," said Joseph. "*You* were the one who made the interpretation, not I."

When Jacob was present, Joseph told his brothers another of his dreams: "I dreamed that the sun and the moon and eleven stars came and bowed down to me."

"Oh, gag me with a spoon," said Judah.

"My son," said Jacob, "are you suggesting that your mother and I and all of your brothers should pay you homage?"

"Dad, it's merely a *dream*," said Joseph disingenuously. "Dreams are but the daytime serial scripts of the unconscious. You can't kill me for having a *dream*."

But killing Joseph suddenly seemed like an intriguing idea to Joseph's older brothers.

"Next time he comes to visit us in the fields, wearing that dorky coat and telling us more of his pre-Freudian dreams," said Simeon, "let's waste the creep."

"Yeah," said Levi, "let's throw him in a pit and tell Dad a wild animal ate him or he was mugged."

All the brothers thought that was a nifty idea, all except for Reuben, who was the oldest, the kindest, and also a well-known delicatessen owner and sandwich inventor.

"Why don't we just throw him in a pit and leave him there?" suggested Reuben.

Reuben figured if they did that, he'd be able to sneak back later, rescue his irritating younger brother, and return him to his father. The others agreed.

But the next time Joseph showed up in the fields, Reuben was away, attending to deli business. His other brothers seized Joseph, tore off his coat of many colors, and threw him in a pit.

"Stop acting out scenarios of sibling rivalry," he called up to them, "and deal with your hostilities in a healthy and productive way!"

The brothers paid Joseph no heed. And when a band of Ishmaelite traders passed by on their way to Egypt, Judah persuaded the others to sell Joseph into slavery for twenty pieces of silver and a dozen Twinkies.

When Reuben returned and learned what they had done to Joseph, he was distraught. The brothers dipped Joseph's coat of many colors in goat's blood and brought it back to Jacob.

"We found this in the fields, Dad," said Zebulun. "Looks like the kid's, but there are too many colors on it now to tell. Is it his or what?"

Jacob nodded, knowing that it was Joseph's. He grieved and wailed and tore his hair and put sackcloth upon his loins and rent his clothes. Then he rent his house as well and went off to Miami for the winter.

# JOSEPH IN EGYPT

**NOW JOSEPH WAS SOLD INTO SLAVERY** in Egypt and found himself in the household of Potiphar, who was during the week a guard for the Pharaoh of all Egypt and on weekends a left tackle for the Cairo Sphinxes. And Joseph outgrew the irritating traits of his youth and matured into a slave wise in the ways of individual psychology, and not only ran Potiphar's household but gave sessions in nondirective psychotherapy and dream interpretation on the side.

One day Potiphar's wife gazed upon Joseph's manly physique and was highly desirous of making moofkie-foofkie with him, but when she informed Joseph of her wish, he said that moofkie-foofkie was out of the question.

And it came to pass that when all of the other servants were out of the house, Potiphar's wife grabbed Joseph by his garments and once more bade him make moofkie-foofkie with her. But Joseph, fearing to be caught in flagrante, tore free of her, leaving his garments in her hands.

And Potiphar's wife did then tell Potiphar that Joseph had been guilty of sexual harassment, and Joseph was sent to a maximum security facility without trial, and bail was set at a figure equal to that of the national debt.

Now it so happened that the Pharoah's chief baker and chief butler were both sent to the maximum-security facility because they had offended their employer. And one night each had a puzzling dream which Joseph entreated them to relate.

"In my dream," said the butler, "I held three vines. They sprouted grapes, and I squeezed them into Pharoah's cup and gave the cup to Pharoah. What does that mean?"

"Well," said Joseph, "the three vines represent three days, and, overlooking the possible sexual symbology of grapes and cups, it means that in three days you'll be sent back to the palace to again be Pharoah's butler. Also I would suggest you put three dollars on a horse named Sprouted Grapes in the Breeder's Cup at Aqueduct."

"If you're right," said the butler, "I'll give you half my earnings and tell Pharoah you're a member of the Psychic Friends Network."

"In *my* dream," said the baker, "I had three baskets on my head full of cakes for Pharoah, but then birds flew down and ate them up. What does that mean?"

"Hmmmm," said Joseph. "It means that in three days Pharoah will chop off your head and hang the rest of you, and vultures will nosh on what's left."

"Oh," said the baker. "And any racing tips?"

Sure enough, Joseph's predictions proved correct. Three days later, Pharoah pardoned his butler and reinstated him at the palace and had the baker decapitated and hung. But the butler, who blew three bucks at Aqueduct when Sprouted Grapes was squeezed out along the rail, never even told Pharoah about Joseph's dream-interpreting abilities.

And it came to pass that one morning two years hence, Pharoah's butler found his master pensive and at loose ends.

"Pardon, sire," said the butler, "but what aileth thee?"

"I've had a dream which vexes me sorely," said Pharoah. "And none of my magicians or seers appears to know what it means."

"Sire," said the butler, "when I was in prison I met there a young Hebrew who does dream interpretation."

"And was he effective?" asked Pharoah.

"He was good at career counseling," said the butler, "not so hot at racing wagers."

"Well, send for him," said Pharoah.

And so Joseph was brought to Pharoah's palace, and Joseph suggested that Pharoah lie down upon a couch and relate his dreams.

"In my first dream," said Pharoah, "I stood upon the bank of a river. And behold, there came up out of the river seven fat cows, and they fed in the meadow. Then out of the selfsame river came seven lean cows, and they devoured the seven fat cows."

"Mmmmm," said Joseph. "And what was the second dream?"

"In my second dream," said Pharoah, "I saw seven fat ears of corn on a stalk. Then seven lean ears of corn emerged, fell upon the seven fat ears and devoured them."

"Mmmmm," said Joseph.

"So what do you think it means?" said Pharoah.

"Well," said Joseph with a frowning smile, "what do *you* think it means?"

Then the face of Pharoah grew cloudy.

"Don't hand me any of that nondirective Freudian crap!" he thundered. "If you know what my dreams mean, tell me!"

"O.K.," said Joseph. "The two dreams are the same. The seven fat cows and the seven fat ears of corn represent seven years of plenty. The seven lean cows and the seven lean ears of corn represent seven years of famine. The dream says that Egypt shall know seven years of plenty, followed by seven years of famine.

"So, were I you, during the next seven plenteous years, I'd take up a fifth of the land and of the corn and grain and other crops and store them up against the seven years of famine which will surely follow. Oh, and put two dollars on Fat Cow on the seventh at Pimlico. And now, I'm afraid, our hour is up."

Pharoah was much impressed by Joseph's interpretation. So much so that he put Joseph in charge of storing Egypt's excess crops for the approaching famine. And Joseph's power increased until it was second only to that of Pharoah himself. And Pharoah arrayed Joseph in garments of red and purple velvet and placed gold chains about his neck, and Joseph looked like either an assistant Pharoah or a rap musician. And Pharoah took off his own ring from his hand and put it on Joseph's hand, and Joseph wondered if that meant they were going steady or what.

And all of this time, Joseph was storing up corn in the storehouses. And finally did the seven plenteous years come to an end and did the seven years of famine begin.

Meanwhile, back in Canaan, Jacob's family had depleted all their stores of food and were reduced to sucking on shirt cardboards for sustenance. In fact, sucking on shirt cardboards was the big meal of the day.

Jacob summoned his sons and said unto them, "Behold, I have heard that there is corn in Egypt. Get you thither and buy us corn." And Joseph's ten brothers went down to buy corn in Egypt, all except little Benjamin.

And Joseph was the governor over the lands, and he it was who sold corn to all the peoples of the land. And Joseph's brethren came unto him and bowed down before him with their faces to the earth, getting grit in their teeth. And Joseph knew his brethren, but they knew him not, because when they saw him last, he was not a governor but a shrimp in a coat of many colors. And Joseph remembered the dream wherein their sheaves had bowed down to his, and he giggled.

And he said unto them, "What do ye wish?"

And they replied, "Corn."

And he said unto them, "What manner of corn do ye seek? Corn on the cob? Carmel corn? Popping corn? Corn such as one findeth upon one's foot, or corn that is humor of poor quality?"

And they said unto him, "All of the above."

And he said, "Nay, ye are spies; to learn the true amount of our corn inventory are ye come."

And they said, "Nay, we are twelve brothers from Canaan, the youngest of which is with our father and the second youngest of which hath met a sorry fate and remaineth an uncleared case at Canaan Homicide."

And Joseph said, "Nay, ye are spies. One of ye must remain with me, the rest go ye to carry corn of all varieties back to Canaan, including humor of poor quality, but bring your youngest brother back unto me."

And Reuben said unto his brothers in a foreign tongue, "Spake I not unto you, saying do not sin against the child, and ye would not hear? Therefore hast this tsuris come down upon us."

And they knew not that Joseph understood them, for they spake in Pig Latin, but Joseph did understand Pig Latin well, for it had been his major in college.

Then Joseph kept from their number his brother Simeon and commanded that his other brothers' sacks be filled with corn preparatory to their departure, and each man's money secretly returned unto his sack.

And the brothers came back to Jacob their father in Canaan and did discover the money in their sacks.

"Vey is mir!" said Reuben. "That man who accused us of being spies will now believe that we are so, and our brother Simeon's ass is grass!"

And Jacob said, "Joseph hath ye taken from me, and then Simeon, and now ye wish to take even little Benjamin. Shlemiels be ye all!"

And famine did prevail in the land of Canaan, and soon was their supply of corn depleted. And the brothers had no choice but to return to Egypt, taking with them their youngest brother, Benjamin.

Stood they once more before Joseph, and they didst tremble with fear of his wrath. But Joseph invited them to dine in his home and gave unto them sustenance and wine and for dessert a tasty sorbet.

And whilst they were dining, Joseph did command the steward of his house to fill the men's sacks with corn, and secretly put every man's money into his sack as before, and Joseph's most treasured silver cup into the sack of Benjamin.

The next morning when the brothers had departed, Joseph dispatched his steward to overtake them on the road, saying, "Wherefore have ye ripped off my master's silver cup?"

And the brothers swore that they had not ripped it off. And the steward said unto them, "He with whom the cup resideth shall become my master's servant, and the others shall be blameless."

And the steward did cause them all to pass their sacks through a metal detector which he had brought with him, and Benjamin's sack did beep. Inside it was the cup discovered.

And the brothers beat their breasts and tore their hair and consumed both Tagament and Xanax. And they were forced to return to Egypt, and stood they once more before Joseph and did weep and puke and carry on in such a fashion that at length Joseph took pity upon them, saying, "All right already. I am Joseph, your brother whom ye did sell into slavery for twenty pieces of silver and a dozen Twinkies."

And at first his brothers believed him not, but then they did, and Joseph fell upon his brother Benjamin's neck and wept, and Benjamin wept upon Joseph's neck, and Joseph kissed all of his brethren and wept upon them, and they upon him, until all of them were sopping wet.

And Joseph said unto them: "Lade your sacks with corn and then get your asses back to Canaan, saying unto our father Jacob, 'Joseph lives and is now a big deal in Egypt.' Then come ye back and ye shall eat the fat of the land, and for those of ye who do eschew fat, shall ye eat a diet rich in fiber and mono-unsaturates."

# MOSES IN THE BULRUSHES

**AND JOSEPH'S BRETHREN** did settle in Egypt, and the children of Israel were fruitful and multiplied and waxed exceedingly mighty in the fields, especially in the fields of stand-up comedy and wholesale ladies ready-to-wear.

Then there arose a new Pharoah in Egypt which knew not Joseph or his brethren, probably because all of them were dead by now, and he did say unto his people, "Behold, the children of Israel are more and mightier than we, also do they possess better connections in show biz. Lest they rise up against us, we shall enslave them and set over them taskmasters to make their lives bitter with hard bondage."

And Pharoah made the children of Israel enter the building trades without a union and build with brick and with mortar the pyramids and the treasure cities and certain shopping malls. And Pharoah said unto his people, "Behold, every daughter that is born to a Hebrew woman shall ye save alive, but every son shall ye cast into the river. Neither shall ye make a little wicker basket for such a baby nor shall ye hide him in the bulrushes."

But contrary to Pharoah's edict, when Jochebed, a Hebrew woman, conceived and bore a son, she did place him in a little wicker basket and take him down to the river and hide him in the bulrushes.

And the baby's sister Miriam did stand not far off to see what would befall him. And Pharoah's daughter came down to the river to bathe and rinse out lingerie and spied the basket. And she looked inside it and cried, "Behold, a Hebrew baby who is fair and without blemish and looketh not unlike a young Charlton Heston! I shall keep him and call him Moses, for I drew him out of the water, and because it is a better name than Him That I Drew Out of the Water."

Then did Miriam approach Pharoah's daughter and say unto her, "I happen to know a Hebrew woman—not his mother or any other blood relative, but someone different—who could nurse him if thou wouldst like." And the Pharoah's daughter replied, "Not a bad little idea; also will I pay her wages and enroll her in an HMO."

And so it came to pass that Moses's mother was able to nurse her own baby and get paid for it, which made her the first Egyptian welfare mother.

Moses grew up, and he observed the suffering of his people at the hands of their taskmasters. One day he saw an Egyptian smiting one of his brethren; he slew the Egyptian and hid his body in the sand. And Moses supposed that no person would know of his deed, yet that evening he heard an account of it on the ten o'clock news, and so he fled to Midian, which had no extradition laws.

# MOSES AND THE BURNING BUSH

**NOW IN MIDIAN**, Moses worked for a man named Jethro, whose daughter Zipporah did become his wife. One day while Moses was tending Jethro's flocks, he spied a bush consumed in flame, and yet the bush was not itself consumed. And a voice did cry out to him, saying, "Moses! Moses!"

And Moses replied, "Yo!"

And the voice in the bush said:

"Moses

"Supposes

"His toses

"Are roses,

"But Moses

"Supposes

"Er-*ro*-ne-ous-ly."

And Moses said, "A bush is reciting jump-rope rhymes to me?"

And the voice in the bush said, "Not the bush, shmuck; *God* is talking to you!  Put thy shoes from off thy feet, for the place whereon thou standest is holy ground."

And although he had not washed his feet in a fortnight, Moses put off his shoes. And God did say unto Moses, "On second thought, put back on thy shoes, for in thy case will I make an exception."

And Moses did replace his shoes. And God continued: "I have surely seen the affliction of my people Israel in Egypt, and I would deliver them from their life of bondage and bring them out of that place into a land flowing with milk and honey and mallomars, and thou shalt be the instrument of my deliverance."

And Moses said, "*Me?*  Why me?"

And God replied, "Because thou slewest the Egyptian who oppressed thy brother, and also because thou looketh a lot like Charlton Heston. I shall send thee to Pharaoh and thou shalt say unto him, 'Let my people go.'"

And Moses replied, "Oh, right; like that's really going to impress him. Nor will he hearken to my voice, for he will say, 'Who art thou to speak to me thus, and what powers dost thou possess?'"

And God said, "Cast thy staff upon the ground."

So Moses did cast his staff upon the ground, and it became a serpent.

"Not bad," said Moses. "How'd you do that?"

"Professional secret," said God. "Now put forth thy hand and grasp the serpent by the tail."

"Eeeooo, gross!" said Moses.

"Do it!" God commanded.

So Moses put forth his hand and grasped the serpent by the tail, and it did become once more his staff.

"Nifty," said Moses. "But how shall I speak to Pharaoh, for I am tongue-tied and far from eloquent."

And God replied, "Is not Aaron the Levite thy brother?"

And Moses granted that this was so.

"Then shall Aaron be thy spokesman to Pharaoh and to the children of Israel," said God, "for not only doth he speak with eloquence but also doth he record voice-overs for nationally advertised products."

# MOSES AND THE PLAGUES

**AND MOSES TOOK HIS BROTHER**, and together they went to Pharaoh. And Moses whispered in Aaron's ear, and Aaron proclaimed, "Thus saith the Lord of Israel: 'Let my people go!'"

And Pharaoh replied, "Who is this Lord that I should obey his voice and let his people go? I know him not nor anyone by that name, except maybe Little Lord Fauntleroy or possibly Jack Lord of *Hawaii Five-O*, which I used to catch in reruns, and I will surely not let his people go."

And Aaron cast down his rod upon the ground before Pharaoh and his magicians and sorcerers, and it became a serpent. Then did Pharaoh's magicians and sorcerers cast down every man his rod upon the ground, and they all became serpents, too, but Aaron's swallowed up their own.

Then did Pharaoh's sorcerers cast down more rods and these did become Slinky Toys. Then did Moses cast down his rod upon the ground, and it became a trash compactor which did devour all the sorcerers' Slinky Toys.

And Moses whispered in Aaron's ear, and Aaron did proclaim unto Pharaoh, "Let my people go, or all of Egypt shall suffer the fate of the Slinky Toys."

And Pharaoh said, "And will thy Lord set upon us a great trash compactor or what?"

And Moses whispered in Aaron's ear, and Aaron said, "No, but things equally distasteful, e.g. turning the waters that are the rivers into blood and causing the fish that liveth therein to die and stink up the place like you wouldn't believe."

And Pharaoh said unto Aaron, "Go and do thy worst, then, and I shall not let thy people go. And by the way, how is it that thou and Moses come here together, but only *thou* doest the talking? Is he Shari Lewis to thy Lambchop or what?"

And so Moses and Aaron left Pharaoh's palace, and God unleashed the first of His plagues, which was a truly Bad Hair Day. Thousands of Egyptians awoke to a total inability to comb or brush their hair or make it lie flat or stand up and follow a natural hairline, and all attempts at rewashing and restyling with a blow-dryer or a mousse availed them not.

Only the hair of the Hebrews was spared such afflictions, and Pharaoh summoned all of his sorcerers to undo the enchantment which the God of the Hebrews had wrought, and all of their efforts availed them not. And a great cry and a gnashing of teeth was heard throughout the land.

And Moses and Aaron returned to Pharaoh, and Pharaoh said unto them, "Thy God is a powerful God. Entreat Him that He may take away the unmanageability of my people's hair, and then shall I let His people go."

And Moses and Aaron left the Pharaoh, and God did according to the word of Moses, and all of the Egyptian people's ability to blow-dry and tease and style their hair was restored to them. And Moses bade the Hebrews prepare to depart in haste from the land of their oppressors.

But when Pharaoh saw that there was respite from the Bad Hair Day, he hardened his heart and harkened not unto his promise and forbade the Hebrews to depart.

And God said unto Moses, "Stretch out thy rod, and I shall

smite the Egyptians now with My next plague, which is the affliction of Dyslexia."

And Moses did so, and all of the Egyptians were thenceforth unable to put a pen to papyrus without involuntarily reversing certain letters from their natural order or to dial toll calls without transposing certain numerals. And Pharaoh summoned his sorcerers to reverse this enchantment as well, but all of their efforts in this regard availed them not.

And Moses and Aaron appeared once more unto Pharaoh, and Aaron said, "Let my people go."

And Pharaoh said, "O.K., O.K., thy God is mightier than I had foreseen. Recall from my people this scourge of dyslexia and then may thy people depart this land to settle in whichever land they choose."

And Moses once more informed the Hebrews that they had been released, and once more they made haste to depart. And Moses raised his rod, and the affliction of dyslexia no more troubled the Egyptian populace.

And Pharaoh, seeing respite from his people's dyslexia, hardened his heart and harkened not to his promise, and once more forbade the Hebrews' departure.

And the Lord said unto Moses, "Now shall My wrath be increased tenfold, and on the morrow shall all Egyptians, but no Hebrews, awake to discover that they have been scheduled by their proctologists for immediate Flexible Sigmoidoscopies."

And the following morning, thousands of Egyptians were forced to submit to a yard of fiber optics being thrust up their nether apertures to scan for polyps or malignant growths of the lower intestine; and Pharaoh himself was unable to avoid such an examination, protest though he might to the royal proctologist; and Pharaoh's sorcerers were unable to undo the enchantment placed upon them by the God of the Hebrews.

And Moses and Aaron did appear to Pharaoh even in the midst of his examination, and Pharaoh said unto them, "The God of the Hebrews is very powerful, indeed. Lift from me this scourge and may thy people depart forthwith from my sight, never to return."

And Aaron raised his rod, and the flexible sigmoidoscopies of thousands of Egyptians were terminated. And Moses said once more to the children of Israel, "Behold, Pharaoh has once more granted us release from our persecution; make haste to depart." And the children of Israel, having known better than to unpack their garment bags after the last plague, were ready, and none were too surprised when Pharaoh once more hardened his heart and changed his mind about releasing them.

Now was God supremely teed off, and did He unleash a succession of grievous plagues upon the Egyptian people, and these did include Fibromyalgia, Chronic Fatigue Syndrome, Jock Itch, Zits, Attention Deficit Disorder, and The Heartbreak Of Psoriasis. And each time did Pharaoh bade the children of Israel depart, and each time did he recall them like defective Pintos.

Finally was God's patience exhausted, and He said unto Moses, "On the morrow I shall bring down yet a final plague upon Pharaoh and upon the Egyptian people, and this one shall be a doozy; and afterwards will he surely let ye go hence and thrust ye out altogether.

"For tonight shall all notary publics go forth and mark the doorposts of the houses of the children of Israel with their special embossed stamps, and on the morrow shall each and every firstborn son of the Egyptians be audited by the Internal Revenue Service, but shall the agents of the IRS see the stamp of the notaries upon the doorposts of the homes of the children of Israel and pass over them; neither shall they be audited nor shall any of their deductions be disallowed, but those of all Egyptians shall be disallowed and subject to all of the interest and penalties accruing thereto. Thus saith the Lord!"

And it came to pass that at daybreak the Lord did smite all of the firstborn sons of the land of Egypt as He had promised, from the firstborn of Pharaoh that sat upon his throne to the firstborn of the captive that was in the dungeon, and all of the firstborn of even cattle, and all of these were audited, and all knew the terror of the unprepared and the undocumented.

And a great cry rose up from the people of Egypt, and a great gnashing of teeth, for none of them was spared. And Pharaoh called for Moses and Aaron yet again, saying unto them, "Rise up and get ye forth from amongst my people, both ye and the children of Israel, and take also thine flocks and thine herds and thine notaries and thine certified public accountants, and begone immediately, if not sooner!"

And the people gathered up all of their possessions and went they to the A&P to buy provisions for the trip, and in their haste did not have time to buy bagels or pumpernickel or pita bread, but grabbed them instead boxes of unleavened Horowitz & Margareten egg matzo, and went out of the land of Egypt and out of the house of bondage and all other kinky fetishes that the children of Israel had in their enslavement been subjected to.

# CROSSING THE RED SEA

**AND IT CAME TO PASS THAT**, when Pharaoh had let the people go, and when the audits of the firstborn had also ceased, that Pharaoh's heart was once more hardened like epoxy glue and that he did slap his forehead and proclaim, "What am I, meshuggeh? To let all of this free labor go and have to hire construction workers at union hourly rates to finish the pyramids, and on Saturdays pay them time-and-a-half? Get real!"

And he made ready the royal chariot and did take with him 600 chariots more, and pursued he after the children of Israel, overtaking them on the shores of the Red Sea where, preparatory to the crossing, they were catching some rays.

And the children of Israel saw Pharaoh and his chariots advancing upon them, and they cried out unto Moses, saying, "Shall we now die at the hands of the Egyptians, and is this preferable to being slaves in Egypt? Thanks a lot!"

And Moses replied unto the Hebrews, saying, "Oh, cease your infernal kvetching!"

Then did Moses stretch out his hands over the Red Sea and then did the Lord cause the sea to go back on both sides and the waters were divided; and the children of Israel followed Moses into the midst of the sea upon dry ground, and the waters were a wall unto them on their right hand and on their left hand, but when they reached the opposite shore did the Angel of the Lord cause them to buy a token and pay a toll.

And the Egyptians did see that the children of Israel were not swallowed up by the sea, but walked they upon dry land, and they did pursue after them to the midst of the sea, with all the king's horses and all the king's men.

But the Lord said unto Moses, "Stretch out thine hand over the sea that the waters may come again upon the Egyptians, upon their chariots, and upon their horsemen."

And Moses stretched forth his hand over the sea, and the water returned. And the Egyptians fled against it, but the waters returned, and they sank as lead in the mighty waves, having between them not so much as a set of water wings.

And Miriam the prophetess, the sister of Moses and Aaron, took a timbrel in her hand, and all the women went out with timbrels and with dances and sang 137 choruses of "John Jacob Jingleheimer Schmidt, That's My Name, Too."

# MOSES IN THE WILDERNESS

**SO MOSES BROUGHT** the children of Israel forth from bondage in Egypt, and they went into the wilderness three days and found there neither water nor food, and all of their supplies of egg matzos were soon depleted. And the people were thirsty and hungry, and there was much complaining, and they said unto Moses, "Would to God we had died in Egypt, where at least we did have ample food, for ye have brought us forth into this wilderness to die of hunger and of thirst."

Then did the Lord cause to rain down from the heavens bread and manna and sausage-and-pepperoni pizza and McDonald's Happy Meals complete with movie-themed toys in little polyethylene bags. And thus did the children of Israel eat for the forty years they wandered in the wilderness, until they came to the land of Canaan, whereupon they were satisfied of hunger but did possess all of them elevated levels of triglycerides and serum cholesterol; and the reason they didst wander in the wilderness for forty years is that Moses took a wrong turn at the intersection of route 87 and the Interstate.

# THE TEN COMMANDMENTS

**AND WHEN THE CHILDREN OF ISRAEL** reached Mount Sinai, God called upon Moses to ascend to the very top of the mountain that He might give unto Moses commandments for the children of Israel to follow in the Promised Land. And when Moses ascended to the peak, God said unto him, "O.K. now, this is just spit-balling, nothing's set in stone yet. By the way, hast thou something upon which to write?"

And Moses replied, "Well, no, sire, I forgot my pen. Shall I go back down and get it?"

And God said, "If thou didst not take a pen, how then didst thou expect to take down My commandments?"

And Moses replied, "Well, I happen to have a nearly photographic memory. Why, are there a lot of them?"

And God replied, "At least seventy or eighty of them, I should estimate."

And Moses said, "Begging your pardon, sire, but less is more."

And God said, "What is that supposed to mean?"

And Moses replied, "I think if You had fewer of them, You might have a better chance of the people actually obeying them."

And God said, "Well, how many would you suggest?"

And Moses said, "If it was me?  I'd give them no more than six."

"And God said, "Six!  Thou art kidding me!  It will take me six just to cover how I am the Lord thy God which have brought them out of the land of Egypt and how they shalt have no other gods before Me or make no graven images nor bow down to them or serve them, blah blah blah, or how I will show mercy to them that loveth Me and keepeth My commandments but visit iniquity upon those of them that hateth Me, or about not taking My name in vain, etcetera etcetera—I mean that's about six right there, am I right?"

"Frankly, sire," said Moses, "I'd skip all that. I mean they *know* You brought them out of Egypt, and they *assume* You would want them to have no other gods before You or that You wouldn't want them to take Your name in vain, and so on. Why state the obvious, You know what I'm saying?"

"So what wouldst *thou* start off with?" said God.

"I'd cut to the chase," said Moses. "I'd right away give them 'Thou shalt not kill, thou shalt not steal, thou shalt honor thy father and thy mother, thou shalt not bear false witness against thy neighbor, and out."

"What about adultery?" said God.

"What about it?" said Moses.

"I mean we have to tell them not to do it," said God.

"Sire," said Moses, "I got to be honest with you, O.K.? That one they are *never* going to buy."

"Maybe not," said God, "but it goes in anyway. Plus one about not coveting thy neighbor's wife."

"But sire," said Moses, "adultery *covers* coveting thy neighbor's wife. Why be redundant?"

And God became impatient. "Look, who's writing these commandments," He said, "thee or Me?"

"Well, actually," said Moses, "I thought *both* of us were."

"That was a rhetorical question," said God. "The Lord God

doth not share a byline nor any writing credit whatsoever."

"How's about an as-told-to?" said Moses.

And God was sorely vexed by this impertinence.

"For thine chutzpah regarding as-told-to credits," said God, "thou shalt not be permitted to enter into the Promised Land! Now, art thou going to take notes on these commandments or art thou not?"

"I *told* you I didn't have a pen," said Moses petulantly, upset to hear that he would not be entering the Promised Land; "neither do I have a notebook or a laptop. What am I supposed to write on?"

"Takest thou a chisel and a hammer and carve them out of *rock* for all I care," said God.

"Fine," said Moses.

# THE GOLDEN CALF

MEANWHILE were the children of Israel at the bottom of Mount Sinai getting restless at the length of Moses's absence.

"What can be taking Moses so long up there?" they cried unto Aaron. "He has been gone now forty days and forty nights."

"God is giving him dictation," said Aaron, "and so far as I know, Moses doesn't know shorthand."

But the children of Israel were impatient and wished to have something they could see to pray to, so Aaron bade them gather together all of their gold jewelry and melt it down, and he fashioned from it a golden calf so that they might have a temp to worship till Moses returned with the real thing.

And it came to pass that Moses finally came down from the top of Mount Sinai, and he was carrying the Ten Commandments in his arms. And then Moses saw the golden calf and saw that the children of Israel were indeed worshipping it instead of the God who had brought them out of bondage in the land of Egypt, and his fury was beyond measure.

He cast the words of the Almighty upon the ground, breaking them into a thousand pieces. And he took the shattered stone commandments and broke them further and ground them to powder and put the powder into water, and made the children of Israel drink of it, and he said unto them, "Take two tablets and call me in the morning."

# SAMSON'S RIDDLE

NOW THERE WAS a certain man of Zorah named Manoah, who had a wife, but children had they none. And an angel of the Lord appeared to the woman and said unto her, "Behold, art thou to bear a son, and he is to be a Nazarite to the Lord, and no razor shall be used upon his head, neither giveth him a mohawk or a buzz-cut, nor shall he use safety razors or Braun cordlesses, for from birth shall the boy belong to God, and he shall save Israel from the Philistines, and he shall be hairy as all get out."

And a son was indeed born to Manoah, and they did call him Samson, and the boy grew to be a strong and powerful young man who pumped iron and won second place in the Mr. Canaan bodybuilders competition.

One day saw Samson a woman in Timnah who was a daughter of the Philistines who had dominion over Israel, and said he unto his parents, "I have seen a woman in Timnah who pleaseth me well; now therefore get her for me to wife." And his parents said unto him, "Is there never a woman amongst the Israelites that pleaseth thee well, that thou must marry a Philistine and a shiksa?"

But Samson persisted, and his parents had spoiled him rotten, so they arranged his betrothal. One day on the way to Timnah to see his betrothed, a young lion came out roaring on the road and did threaten Samson; and such was his strength that Samson was able to rent the lion in twain as one rents in twain a losing Lotto ticket, and Samson did make of the beast road kill.

Several days later, Samson had occasion to again pass the dead lion in the road and observed that there was now a swarm of bees within the lion's carcass; and he took thereof in his hands and ate.

And Samson made a feast for his wedding and said unto thirty companions at the feast, "I will now put forth a riddle to you, and if ye can solve it within the seven days of the feast, then will I give you thirty sheets and thirty changes of garments; and if you cannot solve it then shall ye buy me a Harley-Davidson."

And they said, "Put forth thy riddle that we may solve it."

And Samson said, "Out of the eater came forth meat, and out of the strong came forth sweetness."

And they said, "That's it? That's the riddle?"

And Samson replied unto them, "Yeah, why?"

And the thirty companions said, "Well, we were thinking more along the lines of the traditional 'Why did the chicken cross the road' kind of thing."

And Samson said, "No, that is my riddle."

And his companions thought the riddle stupid, but neither could they solve it; and they approached his wife and said unto her, "Entice thy husband Samson to reveal the answer to his riddle, lest we burn thee and thy father's house, because we're sure not buying Samson a Harley."

And Samson's wife did then try to entice him into revealing the answer to his riddle, weeping before him for seven days, and on the seventh day did he relent and tell her. And told she then the answer to the thirty companions of the feast. And before the sun went down on the seventh day of the feast, they said unto Samson in the fashion of answers given by contestants on *Jeopardy*,

"What is sweeter than honey?  And what is stronger than a lion?"

And Samson was sorely ticked and said unto them, "If ye had not plowed with my heifer, ye had not found out my riddle; but a deal's a deal."

So he went to Ashkelon and smote thirty of its citizens and gave their clothes to the thirty companions who had given the answer to his riddle; but then he also smacked them around a little, because he was still ticked, and he also burned down the cornfields of the Philistines.

Then the Philistines swore vengeance upon Samson for the burning of the cornfields and did force three thousand men of Judah to bind him in new cords and deliver him unto them.

When his captors delivered Samson to the Philistines at a political rally at Lehi, Samson broke the cords that binded him as though they were dental floss. And Samson approached a politician and slew him and took out his jawbone, and with the jawbone of that ass did he slay a thousand Philistines therewith.

And Samson became then a judge of the Israelites and heard their cases and judged them for twenty years; not because his judgments were wise, for indeed they were not, but because the Israelites feared that if they questioned his wisdom, he might tear out somebody's jawbone or something.

# SAMSON AND DELILAH

**AND IT CAME TO PASS ONE DAY** that Samson did fall in love with a woman in the valley of Sorek, and her name was Delilah. And the lords of the Philistines did come to her and said, "Entice Samson, and see wherein his great strength lieth, and by what means we may prevail against him. And if thou art successful, will we give thee eleven hundred pieces of silver and an Amana home freezer."

And Delilah said unto Samson, "Tell me, babe, I pray thee, wherein lieth thy great strength, and wherewith mightest thou be bound to afflict thee?"

And Samson said, "For what purpose dost thou wish to know these things?"

And Delilah said, "Certainly not to tell any Philistines that they might do thee harm."

And Samson said, "Then why?"

And Delilah said, "For kinky pleasures."

So Samson said, "O.K., if thou wilt bind me with seven fresh bowstrings that have not been dried, then shall I be weak as an incumbent president in an election year."

And whilst he slept, she did bind him with seven fresh bowstrings that had not been dried. Then she waked him up, saying, "Samson, the Philistines be upon thee!" and he waked up and broke the bowstrings as easily as if they had been straws.

And Delilah said unto Samson, "Behold, thou hast mocked me and told me lies; how canst we do kinky things if thou escapest thy bindings with such ease?"

And Samson said "If thou bindest me in new ropes that never were occupied, then shall I be weak as other men."

And whilst Samson again slept, Delilah bound him in new ropes. And again she waked him, saying the Philistines were upon him, and he broke them as easily as a newly elected senator breaketh a promise. And she said to him, "Again hast thou mocked me and told me lies; tell me wherewith thou mightest be bound, else I will seek out men with more masochistic tendencies for my play."

And Samson said unto her, "If thou weavest the seven locks of my head with the web, will thou find me weak as a newborn kitten."

And whilst Samson yet again slept, Delilah wove the seven locks of his head with the web, whatever that means; and when she once more shouted that the Philistines were upon him, he once more broke his bonds as if they had been unpresent.

And Delilah pouted and wept and cried that Samson did not love her because he did not reveal to her the source of his strength; and she did pester him so that finally, to quiet her yammering, he said unto her, "O.K., here it is. There hath not come a razor upon mine head, for I am a Nazarite unto God from my mother's womb; and if I be shaven then shall my strength go from me entirely. Now let us proceed with the kinkiness, and it better be worth the trouble."

And again whilst Samson slept did Delilah approach him, and she shaved off all of his hair from his head, making him appear as an NBA basketball player, and his strength went out of him. And Delilah did call the Philistines who came and paid her all that they had promised. And the Philistines took Samson and put out his eyes, and Samson said, "Somehow I expected this to be more fun; so much for kinky pleasures."

And the Philistines took Samson down to Gaza and bound him with fetters of brass and placed him in prison. Howbeit the hair of his head began to grow again after he was shaven, and some of his strength returned, enabling him to pump a little iron on the weight pile in the prison yard, and the prison barber offered to shave the letters of his name into his scalp.

Then the lords of the Philistines gathered together to offer sacrifices to their god, Dagon, and to thank him for delivering Samson into their hands, denying, typically, the efforts of Delilah. And it came to pass that when they were merry and had imbibed much grape that they did send for Samson to make some sport of him. And they brought him up from his cell and stood him upright, the better to mock him.

And Samson said unto the lad who had brought him hence, "Pray, let me feel the pillars whereupon the house standeth, that I might lean upon them."

And the house was filled with more than three thousand men and women who had paid two hundred dollars a plate and were there to be entertained, and they didst call out to Samson, "Pray, say something vulnerable and Jewish and pathetic that we might mock thee!"

But Samson called out silently to the Lord, saying, "Strengthen me only this once that I might be avenged of the Philistines for my two eyes and also for my kinky session with Delilah which never materialized."

And the people called out once more to Samson, saying, "Hey, blind guy, wilt thou entertain us or no?"

And Samson heard them and gave it his best shot and proceeded to bring down the house, and, in the parlance of stand-up comedians, truly killed them.

# RUTH AND NAOMI

**NOW IT CAME TO PASS** that a certain man named Elimelech took unto him a wife named Naomi, and they dwelled in the land of Moab; and Elimelech died, leaving two sons, who did take wives of Moabite women, and their names were Orpah and Ruth. And both sons did die, leaving Naomi, Ruth, and Orpah without husbands and without dates for New Years.

And Naomi decided to return unto the land of Judah from whence she came, and bade each of her daughters-in-law farewell. And Orpah said unto Naomi, "Behold, I shall rearrange the letters in my name and start an afternoon talk show."

But Ruth clave unto Naomi, saying, "Entreat me not to leave thee or to return from following after thee; for whither thou goest, I will go; and where thou lodgest, I will lodge; thy people shall be my people, and thy God my God."

And Naomi replied, "O.K., sure, whatever."

And so did the two women quit Moab and travel to the land of Judah; and there did they settle together.

And one day Naomi got up and made as if to leave, and Ruth said unto her, "Can I follow?"

And Naomi said, "Not this time."

And Ruth was heavy of heart and persisted, saying, "Entreat me not to leave thee, or to return from following after thee; for whither thou goest, I will go; and where thou lodgest, I will lodge; thy people shall be my people, and thy God my God."

And Naomi said unto Ruth, "Hey, I'm just going to the *can*, do you mind? Sheez!"

And Naomi did find Ruth too clingy by half and palmed her off on her cousin Boaz, a wealthy man possessed of many cornfields.

# DAVID AND GOLIATH

NOW THE PHILISTINES did gather together their armies to do battle with the children of Israel in the Valley of the Jolly Green Giant. And King Saul and the men of Israel stood on a mountain on one side, and on the other stood the Philistines, and the Israelites were underdogs, and sorely against them were the odds in Vegas.

And there came out the champion of the Philistines, whose name was called Goliath, and he were a giant measuring six cubits and a span in height, which is taller than Shaquille O'Neal. And he stood and cried out unto the armies of Israel, "Choose ye a man and let him come down to me. And if he be able to fight with me and kill me, then will we be your servants. But if I pre-vail against him and kill him, then shall ye be our servants, and we shall spot you thirty points."

When Saul and the Israelites heard these words, they were greatly afraid. But David, a young shepherd boy, heard Goliath's challenge and said, "I'll fight this man."

And Saul said, "Thou canst not fight with him; thou art but a stripling. What other man in my army will engage this giant in battle?"

And every man in Saul's army did glance elsewhere and become invested in other activities. And Saul said, "That being the case, stripling, why not give it a shot?"

And Saul armed David with his armor, and put a helmet of brass upon his head, and also gave him a sword and a coat of mail. And David said unto Saul, "What use have I for a helmet that looketh like a spittoon and a coat made of old letters and postcards?" And he put these off of him and advanced into the valley to meet the Philistine.

And when the giant saw David, he disdained him, saying, "Who art thou to do battle with Goliath, an unarmed stripling bigger not than Muggsy Bogues?"

And the Philistine drew nigh unto David and raised his

sword, and David rummaged about in his mind and chose five smooth epithets and hurled them at the giant along with bitter invective and scathing sarcasm. And the invective did blind Goliath with rage, and the sarcasm did cause second-degree burns upon his skin, and the epithets struck him forcibly in his fragile ego, causing him to sink to his knees and fall upon his face to the earth. And David stood over the Philistine, and drew the giant's sword, and cut off his head, and brought it back as a souvenir.

But it was an unwieldy thing and fitteth not upon David's key chain and was soon replaced by a rabbit's foot.

# THE WISDOM OF SOLOMON

**WHEN KING SAUL FELL** in battle with the Philistines, David was crowned king of Israel, also was a hotel in Jerusalem named in his honor. And when David died, his son Solomon became the king; and Solomon was a wise king, and his wisdom was known throughout the land.

Then came to Solomon two women, and one said to him, "My lord, I and this woman dwell in one house, and I was delivered of a child in this house; and this woman was delivered of a child as well. And this woman's child died during the night, and she took my child from me whilst I slept and laid it in her bosom, and took her dead child and laid it in mine, and the trade pleaseth me not."

And the second woman said, "Nay, but the living son is mine, and the dead one is thine." And the first woman said, "You're full of it; it's the other way around," and so on.

Then said King Solomon, "Bring me a sword," and a sword was brought unto the king. And Solomon said, "Divide the living child in twain, and give half to the one and half to the other, and save the sweetbreads for me."

Then spoke the first woman, saying, "That solution may at first blush seem cruel, but it is, upon further reflection, absolutely brilliant. I'd like the top half."

And the second woman spoke, saying, "Not for nothing, sire, hast thy wisdom been universally touted. But it is *I*, as the true mother of the child, who deserve the top half."

Then spoke King Solomon to his courtiers, saying, "In no wise slay this child, but find for it a home in my court; following which, take ye this sword and put both of these harridans out of their misery."

And this was done, and all of Israel heard of the judgment which Solomon hath meted out; and they figured, Hey, what the heck, the guy's king, let him do what he wants.

# JONAH AND THE WHALE

**NOW THE WORD OF THE LORD** came unto Jonah, saying, "Arise, Jonah, and go to Nineveh and cry out against it, for their wickedness vexes me sorely."

And Jonah said, "When was it you wished me to do this?"

And the Lord said, "At first light."

And Jonah feared to go to Nineveh and cry out against it, and said unto God, "At first light I have that breakfast meeting, and afterwards an appointment at the dermatologist, and the rest of the day is pretty much booked, too."

And the Lord was displeased with Jonah's response.

And Jonah fled from the presence of the Lord and went down

to Joppa, there to board a cruise ship for Tarshish. But the Lord sent out a great wind into the sea, and created He a mighty tempest to rock the boat wherein Jonah hid from his God.

And the mariners aboard the ship were greatly frightened and did cry out every man unto his god.

And Jonah went down into the hold of the ship to hide. And the shipmaster came unto Jonah and said, "All of the lads are calling unto their gods for help in this storm so that we do not perish, and we wondered if you could sort of call unto yours, too."

And Jonah said, "My God happens to be vacationing this week on the Vineyard or I sure would."

And the shipmaster said, "Well, doesn't He possess a beeper?"

And Jonah said, "If He does, the number isn't published."

And the mariners said, "Come, let us cast lots that we may know for whose cause this evil is upon us."

So they cast lots, and the lot fell upon Jonah; and they said unto Jonah, "Wherefore comest this tempest and whence comest thou and what is thy religious affiliation, while we're on the subject?"

And Jonah was beset by guilt over what had befallen his shipmates on his account and replied unto them, "I am a Hebrew, and my God is the same one that created the heaven and the earth."

And they replied, "Oh yeah, that one."

And Jonah said, "This is happening because He wanted me to go to Nineveh and cry out against their wickedness, and I had other stuff to do."

And the mariners and passengers said unto him, "What shall we do unto thee that the sea may be again calm to us and not tempestuous nor causeth us to toss our cookies without ceasing?"

And Jonah said, "Oh, take me up and cast me forth into the sea, so shall it be calm again for you, I guess."

And they said unto him, "That is thoughtful of you, and we would not do so were there other options."

And they cast him into the sea along with his fanny pack, and the sea did immediately swallow him up and cease her raging.

And the Lord caused a great fish to swallow up Jonah; and Jonah was in the belly of the fish for three days and three nights, and there was naught for him to do in there, for the great fish possessed in its belly neither reading matter nor even so much as a Ping-Pong table.

Then Jonah cried out unto the Lord from the belly of the beast and said, "Thou cast me into the deep in the midst of the seas, and I was wrong to have tried to escape thine entreaty to go to Nineveh; and if thou wouldst reconsider, I will now gladly do so, assuming that better transportation than this might be available."

And the Lord heard Jonah's prayer and spoke unto the great fish, and the great fish did then vomit Jonah out onto dry land, along with a case of fortnight-old sushi it had unwisely consumed the night before.

# SHADRACH, MESHACH, AND ABEDNEGO

**AND IT CAME TO PASS** that Nebuchadnezzar, king of Babylonia, caused an idol of gold to be made whose height was threescore cubits and whose breadth was six cubits, and it was originally made as a prop for a video, but afterwards Nebuchadnezzar decided to have his people worship it.

And a herald of the king did cry out, "To you it is commanded that at whatsoever time ye hear the sound of the cornet, the flute, the harp, the sackbut, the psaltery, and the dulcimer, ye fall down and worship the golden idol that the king hath set up.

And whoso falleth not down and worshippeth shall that same hour be thrown into the midst of a fiery furnace which has been specially constructed to process the unobservant."

"Next thing you know," said Artie Shadrach, an attorney with the firm of Shadrach, Meshach & Abednego, "he's going to insist on prayer in public schools."

Being Jewish, Shadrach, Meshach, and Abednego did all three of them refuse to worship the golden idol. And Nebuchadnezzar heard about this and ordered the men to be brought before him.

"Is it true," said Nebuchadnezzar, "that when ye hear the sound of the cornet, the flute, the harp, the sackbut, the psaltery, and the dulcimer, ye refuse to worship the golden idol I have set up?"

"Being Jews, and worshipping only our one true God," said Meshach, "we do so refuse."

"Besides which," said Abednego, "who even knows what a sackbut or a psaltery *are*, much less what they sound like?"

"If ye do not worship my golden idol," shouted Nebuchadnezzar, "ye shall at once be thrown into this fiery furnace!"

"O King," said Shadrach, "we shall not worship thy stupid idol; and if thou dost throw us into this or any other fiery furnace, not only will our God save us, but afterwards we shall sue thine ass."

And Nebuchadnezzar ordered the thermostat be turned up and the furnace heated seven times hotter than usual; and then Shadrach, Meshach, and Abednego were cast into the fiery furnace.

And the furnace was so hot that the flames consumed the soldiers who had cast them into its depths; but Shadrach, Meshach, and Abednego were untouched by the flames and did complain even of a draft.

And Shadrach said, "Do you suppose this be gas heat or oil, and which of the two doth burn cleaner and with less cost to the consumer?"

And Meshach said, "I happen to have brought with me marshmallows, graham crackers, and Hershey bars if anyone would like s'mores."

And Abednego said, "Campfires always make me want to sing," and led the others in a medley of the Beach Boys greatest hits, beginning with "Little Deuce Coupe."

And Nebuchadnezzar could not believe the evidence of his eyes and ordered the men to come out. And Shadrach, Meshach, and Abednego emerged from the fire, and Nebuchadnezzar saw that the hair on their heads was not singed and their cloaks were not burnt and even their marshmallows were not blackened enough to make the centers runny.

And Nebuchadnezzar said, "Blessed be the God of Shadrach, Meshach, and Abednego, who saveth his servants when they refused to obey the king's orders. I command that anyone who sayeth anything against the God of Shadrach, Meshach, and Abednego be cut up into pieces."

And Shadrach, Meshach, and Abednego thanked the king for his sentiments, but they sued his ass anyway and won.

# MENE MENE TEKEL UPHARSIN

**AND KING BELSHAZZAR**, son of Nebuchadnezzar, replaced his father and ruled Babylonia; but Belshazzar was an arrogant king, and at a drunken banquet did he mock the God of the Hebrews by drinking from the sacred vessels which his father had filched from the Temple at Jerusalem.

In the same hour did a mysterious hand appear and begin to write graffiti upon the wall of the banquet hall. Then did the king's countenance change, and his knees smote one against the other, and the king soiled himself.

And he cried out for his astrologers and his soothsayers, and he spoke to the wise men of Babylon, saying, "Whosoever shall read this writing and show me the interpretation thereof shall be clothed in scarlet and have a chain of gold about his neck and other perks befitting the third ruler in the kingdom."

Then came in all the king's wise men, and all of them did try to read the handwriting on the wall.

Said one, "O King, this handwriting is decipherable to me."

And the king replied, "Say on."

And the wise man continued, "The slant is backward, sire, indicating that head ruleth heart; but the loops are open, denoting a friendly and garrulous nature; also doth the handwriting proceed on a downward slant, which suggesteth that the writer is of a strongly pessimistic bent."

"Yes, but what of the content?" said the king.

"Oh, of that am I clueless," replied the wise man.

And this response pleased not Belshazzar, who had the man beheaded.

Now the queen came into the banquet hall and said, "O King, there be a man in thy kingdom in whom thy father Nebuchadnezzar placed great trust, and he was able to interpret dreams and do the *New York Times* crossword puzzle in ink. And his name be Daniel, a Hebrew prophet be he, and if thou callest him here, will he surely interpret the handwriting."

Then was Daniel brought before the king, and the king said unto him, "If thou canst read this writing and make known to me the interpretation thereof, thou shalt be clothed in scarlet and have chains of gold about thy neck, and be third ruler in the kingdom, with a parking place unto which hath been sprayed thy name directly on the blacktop."

And Daniel said, "Scarlet doth make my skin to appear sallow; gold chains about the neck are for dealers in controlled substances; and I have no need of parking places with my name upon them for God Himself doth validate my parking; yet will I read it anyway."

And Daniel read the handwriting on the wall aloud: "Mene mene tekel upharsin."

And the king said, "Many many tickle a parson?"

And Daniel said, "'Mene mene tekel upharsin.' It means that thou hast been an arrogant and foolish king, that thou hast mocked God by drinking out of the holy vessels that thy father didst filch from the Temple of Jerusalem; that God hath weighed thee in the balances and found thee wanting; that thy kingdom hast been divided and given to the Medes and the Persians; that thine hours upon this earth are numbered and few."

"Uh huh, well, that's kind of a downer," said Belshazzar. "Oboy, look at the time. Hey, I'm going up to bed, but stick around and have a couple crème de menthes at the bar there if you like. I'm buying."

# ESTHER, THE WHOLE MEGILLAH

**IN THE COUNTRY OF PERSIA**, in the capital city of Shushan, there lived a king named Ahoshvayros. If he had lived in Cedar Rapids, his name probably would have been Fred.

The king loved parties, but his queen, Vashti, had tired of them. At one of these parties, the king sent for Vashti; but she had just taken two Tylenols and lain down for a snooze, so she sent her regrets.

"Are you ready for this?" roared the king, "a queen too pooped to party? Tell Vashti either she shows up at my party or she is *history*!"

"I'll tell her, sire," said the messenger, "but don't kill me if it doesn't work."

The messenger went to Vashti.

"Vashti," said the messenger, "King says either party or suffer serious consequences."

"The one thing you really want to hear when you have a headache the size of Philadelphia is threats," said Vashti. "Tell the king I'm snoozing."

"You don't mind my saying so," said the messenger, "not showing up at the party is a deal-breaker."

"Then let the deal be broken," said Vashti. "Frankly, being queen isn't all it's cracked up to be."

When the king heard Vashti's reply, he banished her from his kingdom and canceled all her credit cards. But after the party was over, the king became lonely without a queen to be nasty to.

"I miss old Vashti," he said, "even though she didn't party. She smelled good. But I shall find a new queen, who will smell even better. Send word throughout Persia that I'm holding a beauty contest. The winner shall be queen with all the perks."

Word went forth. All the women in Persia wanted to win the contest and become queen. All but a young Jewish woman named Esther, who was not only beautiful but a CPA.

"Enter the contest," said Esther's wise cousin Mordecai.

"What do I need to be queen for?" said Esther. "I'm a CPA. The hours are great, I make a living, and I do my own tax returns."

"From what I hear," said Mordecai, "a queen's hours are even better. Plus which, if you were queen, you could help the Jewish people, who could use a little help at this particular point in time."

"Morty," said Esther, "I'd rather help the Jewish people than anything, but I can't give up a comfortable practice in accounting."

Mordecai grabbed his chest and inhaled sharply.

"What is it?" asked Esther, alarmed.

"A heart broken by a cousin's unwillingness to think of anybody but herself," said Mordecai.

Jewish guilt washed over Esther like a tidal wave.

"O.K., Morty," she sighed, "I'll give it a shot."

So Esther entered the contest. Everyone in Persia turned out to watch.

For the talent part Esther tap-danced to Beethoven's Ninth. Then she performed *Macbeth*, playing all the roles herself. By the third hour of her performance, the king was snoring so loudly it broke Esther's concentration. But when the bathing suit part of the competition began, the king perked right up again.

"Behold," said the king, "Esther is the most talented woman in all of Persia. Tell me, dear, do you like to party?"

"Not that much," said Esther.

"May I have a word with her, sire?" said Mordecai.

"If you're quick about it," said the king.

"Esther, may I suggest a different answer to the partying question," whispered Mordecai, "such as 'Sire, my motto is "Boogie till you drop"'?"

"But my motto is 'Idle hands are the devil's playground,'" Esther protested.

"Oh, Essie, they're so *close*," whispered Mordecai. "Why not stretch the truth a tiny bit?"

"Can we dispense with the whispering and get on with the show?" said the king irritably.

"I cannot tell the king a *fib*," said Esther.

"A wise man once said 'Better a small fib than a huge truth,'" whispered Mordecai.

"Who said that?" whispered Esther.

"Me," said Mordecai, "just now."

"Morty," said Esther, "I can't—"

Mordecai grabbed his chest in pain.

"O.K., Morty, O.K.," sighed Esther.

Wise cousin Mordecai scurried offstage.

"Esther," said the king, "do you like to party or not?"

"My motto," said Esther, "is 'Boogie till you drop.'"

"I now pronounce Esther the hands-down winner and new queen!" said the king.

Everyone in Persia shouted for joy. Everyone but the woman who'd been named Miss Congeniality, and she kicked Esther in the shins.

"A word to the wise," whispered Mordecai to Esther. "Don't tell anyone you're Jewish yet."

King Ahoshvayros and Queen Esther set sail for Acapulco, leaving Persia to the king's nasty prime minister, Haman.

Because Haman was prime minister, he ordered everyone in Persia to bow down to him. Everyone did, everyone but Mordecai.

"Why do you not bow down to me?" asked Haman.

"Well," said Mordecai, "outside of I personally consider you to be a vartlet and a shmendrick, I don't bow down to *any* man. Jews bow down only to God."

This reply irked Haman. Let one guy not bow down, pretty soon others would follow. Before you knew it, nobody would bow down, in which case what was the point of being prime minister?

Haman decreed that Mordecai and all the Jews in Persia be put to death. He cast lots, or *purim*, to pick a day for the killing. The day Haman chose was the thirteenth day of Adar. Although Haman was prime minister, anytime he wanted to do something like kill Jews, he needed permission. So he faxed Acapulco: "Dear King, I plan to kill all the Jews on the thirteenth of Adar, if that's convenient for you and the missus. Love, Haman."

"The thirteenth of Adar," said the king, checking his calendar. "I don't have anything doing that day, so fine." Esther, of course, knew nothing about this.

When Esther and Ahoshvayros returned from their honeymoon, Mordecai met them at the boat.

"Hate to ruin your day," he whispered to Esther, "but Haman's planning to kill all the Jews on the thirteenth of Adar. It's time to tell the king you're a Jew and plead for our people's lives."

"Ahoshvayros picked up a bug in Mexico," said Esther. "He's been running to the john forty times a day. I go to him now and say I'm Jewish, I've had it."

"Comes the thirteenth of Adar, bubbeleh," said wise cousin

Mordecai, "you've had it anyhow."

Esther went to see the king. She was nervous.

"Why have you come to see me?" said the king.

"Why have I come to see you?" said Esther. "To, uh . . . invite you and Haman to dinner Saturday."

The king checked his Filofax.

"Saturday is cool," he said. "You want to make something festive?"

"What I'll make is reservations," said Esther.

"Isn't that an old joke?" said the king.

"Not yet," said Esther.

Meanwhile, Mordecai overheard two royal servants plotting to kill the king. Although Ahoshvayros was not a great king, Esther's marriage had made him Mordecai's cousin, and Mordecai wasn't *about* to let anybody kill his cousin. Mordecai phoned the king.

"Hi," said a voice, "this is the king. I can't come to the phone now, but if you leave your name and number, I'll get right back to you."

Mordecai left a message: "Hi, sire, I hate to be a tattletale, but two of your servants are plotting to kill you. Have a nice day. Mordecai."

The king got Mordecai's message and realized Mordecai had saved his life. He wanted to reward him, but couldn't think how.

"Maybe a nice pen-and-pencil set with 'Compliments of the King' engraved on it," he thought. Nah. Saving a king's life deserved better. He sent for Haman.

"Haman," said the king, "I'd like to do something nice for one of my most loyal subjects. Any ideas?"

Haman thought the king wanted to reward *him* and was very pleased.

"Sire," said Haman, "I'd have this man dressed in the king's own robes and crown, and I'd have him placed on the king's own horse and led through the streets of Shushan by the king's representative, who'd proclaim, 'Thus shall be done to the man whom the king delights to honor!'"

"Splendid idea, Haman," said the king.

"Thank you, sire," said Haman. "And who is this man you wish to honor?"

"Mordecai," said the king. Haman was totally bummed.

"Haman, you look a little under the weather," said the king.

"I think it was something I ate," said Haman.

"Boy, do I know what *that's* like," said the king. "You want to borrow some Pepto-Bismol?"

And so the very next day, Haman was forced to dress Mordecai in the king's robes and crown, seat him on the king's horse, and parade him through Shushan, proclaiming, "Thus shall be done to the man whom the king delights to honor!"

Haman was pissed. Mordecai giggled the whole time.

Saturday night Ahoshvayros, Esther, and Haman went to a Japanese restaurant. After they'd had several drinks, the king got peppy.

"Esther," he said, "I'm prepared to give you anything you wish, doll—even half my kingdom."

"I don't want half your kingdom," she replied. "All I want is for you to spare my life."

"Run that past me again, Essie," he said.

The waiter approached the table.

"Somebody's planning to kill me," said Esther.

"You folks wish to order now?" asked the waiter.

"Nobody's planning to kill *you*," said the king. "Somebody was planning to kill *me*, but I caught them."

"No, no," she said, "somebody's definitely planning to kill *me*."

"Somebody I know?" said the king.

"You folks need a little more time?" said the waiter.

"Not only do you know him," said Esther, "but he's here with us at this very table."

The king grabbed the waiter.

"Are you trying to kill my wife?" he shouted.

"Not the *waiter*, dummy!" yelled Esther.

The king released the waiter and grabbed Haman.

"Are you trying to kill my wife?" he shouted.

"N-no, sire," stuttered the hapless Haman.

The king released Haman, who collapsed with relief.

"See, hon?" said the king, "nobody at this table is planning to kill you."

"Yeah?" said Esther. "Then tell me, Haman, on the thirteenth of Adar do you plan to hang all the Jews in Persia—yes or no?"

"Uh, the thirteenth of Adar . . . " said Haman, stalling for time. "What day of the week does that fall on?"

"Are you killing all the Jews of Persia on the thirteenth of Adar or not?" Esther persisted.

"If it's a Thursday, I may be," said Haman. "Somehow the *fourteenth* is what sticks in my mind, though."

"What's the point here, Essie?" said Ahoshvayros, slapping the cheeks of the fainted waiter.

"The point," said Esther, "is if Haman kills all the Jews, then he kills me, too. Because, I, Esther, queen of Persia, am Jewish!"

"Funny, you don't *look* Jewish," said the king.

"I thought you were Unitarian," said Haman.

"Haman," said the king, "this time you definitely put your foot in it."

The waiter regained consciousness.

"What are your orders?" he asked.

"My orders," said the king, "are three sushi specials, three hand rolls, three seaweed salads, and that on the thirteenth of Adar, Haman gets hanged on the very gallows on which he was planning to kill Mordecai."

"Very well, sire," said the waiter. "And miso soup comes with that, too."

The Jews of Persia learned they were saved, and they held a humongous celebration in Queen Esther's honor.